THE WHISPERED MYSTERY

DANIEL TORRES

THE ASTRAL ADVENTURES OF ROCCO VARGAS 2

catalan communications
new york

THE WHISPERER MYSTERY
ISBN 0-87416-096-0

The Astral Adventures of Rocco Vargas, 2
Written and illustrated by Daniel Torres

Translated from the Spanish original,
"El Misterio de Susurro", by David
H. Rosenthal. Edited by Bernd Metz

Published by Catalan Communications
43 E. 19th Street
New York, NY 10003

© 1990 Daniel Torres, Rights managed
by NORMA EDITORIAL, Barcelona

English language edition © 1990 Catalan Communications

Series design concept: Marigot

First Catalan Communications edition, May 1990
10 9 8 7 6 5 4 3 2 1

Dep. L. B. 9050/90
Printed in Spain by NORMA SERVEIS GRÀFICS

Write to us for a free catalogue of our graphic novels.

SEPTEMBER 23, 1983. AS AUTUMN COMES TO SOME PARTS OF EARTH, HERE ON RHEA- SATURN'S SIXTH MOON - LEAVES WON'T TOUCH THE GROUND. DEAD BODIES WILL BLOCK THEM.

OCTOBER 3RD. SING-SING FALLS. THE VENUSIAN TROOPS HAVE PAID HEAVILY FOR THEIR "EXCURSION". BUT EVERYTHING HAS ITS BRIGHT SIDE. A LOT OF BOOKS WILL BE WRITTEN ABOUT THIS BATTLE.

HISTORIANS WILL FILL AS MANY PAGES AS THERE ARE HELMETS PILED IN THE VALLEY.

October 4, 1983

News from the Front

Lynx, Mega

Every ditch is piled high with helmets. Twenty-five years have passed since the end of the great space war, but the ditches have never been cleared of helmets. That's what happens when a moon is divided.

During this entire time, Venus has tried to win back its former colony. Its shows of force were ineffective: a display of military might that ran into a wall of North Rheamite resistance, a declaration of war—in January of this year—that brought it up against a surprisingly powerful army.

Now, after the rout at Sing-Sing, negotiation is the only way to end a war other planets want nothing to do with. Even Earth, which has given economic aid to the Megavenus government, observes the colonial power's death throes from a distance.

①

By Occupying Sing-Sing, Venus Tried to Split North Rhea

News from the Front

Lynx, Megavenus (Rhea)

Here in North Rhea, faced with rugged terrain and determined troops, the Venusians' conventional military tactics are useless. Venus's chiefs of staff couldn't or refused to realize that occupying the valley wouldn't create a siege. No one really knew what would happen at Sing-Sing.

The garrison consisted of the 3rd and 4th Venusian occupying fleets. The trap snapped shut. The North Rheamites attacked on September 23rd with an army whose size the generals in the Venusian rear had never expected. These furious attacks were devastating. Within a few days, Sing-Sing was reduced to an outpost in its center and a spaceport that was almost useless. The counterattack never occurred. The Venusian troops could feel the enemy breathing down their necks. On October 3rd, the North Rheamites only had to advance a few feet before their enemies surrendered.

How could they have let themselves be caught like rats in a trap? More than 80% of the Venusian troops perished. 75% of these casualties were caused by the North Rheamite space artillery. A threat no one had foreseen.

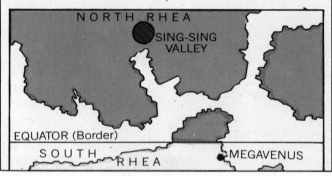

News from the Front

Lynx, Megavenus (Rhea)

Peace Conference in Vantam: Talk Talk, Fight Fight

The Venusian administration is committing an error when it fails to recognize that a stable government is needed to maintain its colony in South Rhea. And the government of Megavenus is extremely shaky. The populace has no faith in it.

For this reason, many doubt that the conference will lead to peace. Some affirm that today the only way open is not diplomatic but military. Can they be right? What can be the use of this conference if both sides seek to fortify their positions not at the negotiating table but through raids and guerrilla tactics?

THE "MONGO", A GREAT PLACE TO SPEND A NIGHT ON EARTH.

THOUGH FOR SOME PATRONS, MORNING NEVER COMES.

OH! I CAN'T ESCAPE DUDUA...HIC! MY FEET GET TANGLED IN HER LACE... I CAN'T WALK STRAIGHT...

SILK... HIC! COCKTAILS AND MY FEET... DOOBIE DOOBIE DA... TRAPPED!

③

TAC!

GOTCHA!

FIVE TO FOUR, SIR!

I OWE YOU A DINNER, SAMSON.

THE MAILMAN!

MAIL FOR ARMANDO MISTRAL.

AHA!

♫

LETTERS FOR RUBY... "THE METEOR", AND... GASP!! THE NEW "SCIENCE FICTION" IS OUT...

WITH SAM'S LATEST ADVENTURES!

CIENCIA Y ficción

N73 ● NOVIEMBRE 1483

Sam Horton

POR ARMANDO MISTRAL

THIS PACKAGE LOOKS PROMISING. IT'S FROM JILL COVALSKY ON URANUS.

LET'S GO IN. GUESS WHAT I NEED RIGHT NOW.

COFFEE, SIR, COFFEE.

4

JILL SAYS SHE'S VERY HAPPY. SHE'S WORKING IN THE PETROSSIAN INSTITUTE OF SPACE PHYSICS. AH! SHE SENT YOU A PRESENT. "FOR LITTLE SAMSON."

IT'S A TOY THAT'S ALL THE RAGE ON URANUS, BUT SHE'S BUILT A FEW SURPRISES INTO IT.

SHE CALLED ME LITTLE?

IT'S CALLED COSMO.

LITTLE!!

I'LL ACTIVATE IT ACCORDING TO THE INSTRUCTIONS.

CLIC!

KIP!

CUTE, HUH?

CUTER THAN A BUG'S EAR, I'D SAY.

AAAH!

KIP

MY COFFEE!

LOOK!

MMM! DELICIOUS!

I HOPE HE KNOWS HOW TO MAKE TOAST. I'VE JUST FORGOTTEN.

⑤

HELLO, BOYS! "SCIENCE FICTION" IS OUT!

BOYS, HUMPH! I'LL GO BUY DIAPERS.

WHAT'D HE SAY?

THAT HE'S ALL EXCITED, RUBY.

LOOK WHAT HE GOT!

OH! HOW SWEET!

I DON'T LIKE DOLLS!!

SPEAKING OF DOLLS, WHAT'S THAT CHICK UP TO WITH SAM NORTON?

A DANGEROUS GAME! SHE'S TRYING TO GET HIM INTERESTED. TODAY I HAVE TO FINISH THE NEXT INSTALLMENT.

WHAT DO YOU THINK?

I THINK SAM'LL END UP FALLING FOR THAT DARING STELLA STAR.

Enemig

RUBY'S NOT THE ONLY ONE IN TOWN WITH AN OPINION...

WHAT A GUY, SAM NORTON. HE WOULDN'T FALL FOR JUST ANY SEXY BROAD.

J. CUPER INVESTIGACIONES

6

ARMANDO MISTRAL MUST HAVE A BLAST WRITING ALL THOSE LIES.

WHILE I SPEND ALL DAY TRYING TO FIGURE OUT WHERE MY MONEY GOES.

WHAT IF I TOOK A SHOT AT IT? WHY NOT? WHO'S STOPPING ME FROM WRITING NOVELS ABOUT EVEN MORE EXCITING CASES?

WHAT CASES?

KNOCK, KNOCK!

AHEM, WOULD YOU PERMIT MY HUMBLE PERSON TO STEP INSIDE THIS TEMPLE OF WISDOM?

GET TO WORK, PAL. YOUR FIRST BOOK JUST ARRIVED.

COULD ONE AS INSIGNIFICANT AS CHOP JONES BE LUCKY ENOUGH TO INDUCE THE FEARSOME ARCHIBALD COOPER TO ACCEPT A MISSION?

I NEVER LEARN.

AN ELEMENTARY TASK FOR YOUR BOUNDLESS TALENTS. ALL YOU HAVE TO DO IS GO TO "HEROES AND PIRATES" THIS AFTERNOON... A KROP-DEN IN PORT NINE.

SO FAR, SO GOOD.

PORT NINE! THAT NEIGHBORHOOD USUALLY LEAVES YOU WITH A HANGOVER THAT LASTS FOR DAYS.

WHEN YOU GET THERE, ASK FOR THE BOSS AND TELL HIM: "I KNOW ABOUT THAT BUSINESS WITH THE KOO LEGION." THAT'S ALL.

WHAT IS YOUR SAGE REPLY?

I WAS ABOUT TO GET NOSY ABOUT THIS FUNNY BUSINESS WHEN I SAW THE BULGE UNDER HIS JACKET.

WHAT IF I'M TIRED?

IN THAT CASE, I HOPE THIS TRIFLING ADVANCE WILL RESTORE THE STRENGTH TO YOUR MIGHTY MUSCLES.

VERY THOUGHTFUL.

REMEMBER, THIS AFTERNOON.

⑦

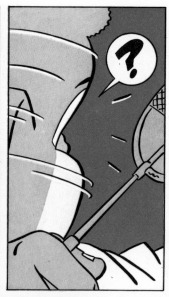

LOST IN MEMORIES...

...ROCCO ARRIVES IN MONTEBAHIA.

A CITY WHERE YOU CAN LOSE YOUR BLUES AMONG A MILLION STORIES.

HERE I WAS IN PORT NINE, THE LAST PLACE ON EARTH YOU'D WANT YOUR MOTHER TO LIVE.

AT LEAST I WAS PREPARED. I GAVE MY GUN A FULL DOSE.

AND I FOLLOWED OLD JONES'S INSTRUCTIONS AND LOOKED FOR "HEROES AND PIRATES."

11

I WANT A BOOK ABOUT SUCCESS.

GO LOOK.

A COZY SPOT. THE CUSTOMERS WERE ALL TAKING MOON-WALKS WITHOUT SPACE SUITS.

I CARRIED OUT MY ORDERS.

THE BOSS HERE?

THAT'S ME.

...AND TOLD HIM!

I KNOW ABOUT THAT BUSINESS WITH THE KOO LEGIONS.

?!

IMPRESSED, HUH?

I DIDN'T LIKE HOW HE LOOKED AT ME.

SOMETHING TOLD ME I WAS GOING TO GET MY SHIRT WRINKLED.

WAIT A MOMENT...

12

15

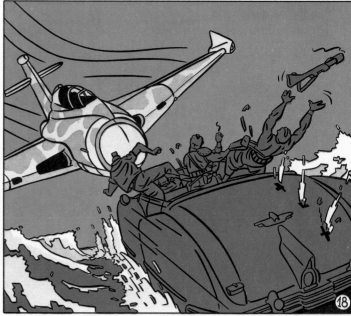

A FEW COCKTAILS LATER...

...AND THAT'S ALL. OLD CHOP JONES WITH HIS FANCY TALK AND HIS ADVANCE GOT ME INVOLVED IN SOME FUNNY BUSINESS.

I TOLD THEM THE LITTLE I KNEW.

IN THIS TOWN, YOU NEVER KNOW WHAT KIND OF TROUBLE THEY'RE TRYING TO GET YOU IN.

THAT'S WHY I CAN'T FIGURE OUT WHERE THAT BROAD CAME FROM OR WHY ALL THE GUNPLAY.

BROADS AND GUNPLAY? THAT'S ALMOST PERFECT.

DON'T PUT YOURSELF OUT, ARCHIE. I DON'T CARE ABOUT THE GIRL, THE DRUGS, OR THE GUY WITH THE FIREARM FOR AN ARM. BUT WHY WERE THE COPS AFTER US?

THEY MUST HAVE THOUGHT WE WERE KROP DEALERS!

DON'T BE A FOOL AND DON'T TALK AS IF I WERE ONE. YOU KNOW COMMISSIONER SINO'S BLOODHOUNDS ONLY GO AFTER BIG GAME!

TELEPHONE, MR. MISTRAL.

THANKS, NESTOR.

YES?

PSST... DON'T GET FRIENDLY WITH THAT SNOOP... PSST... OR YOU'LL END UP LIKE HIM... PSST... DEAD!!

20

AAGG...

GGG...

°o

A HARPOON!

IT CAME FROM THE BEACH.

CAN'T SEE A THING.

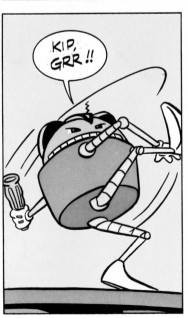

KIP, GRR!!

TOC

UNK!

III!

21

23

CLICK!

BLAM!

CLICK!

WHAT ROTTEN LUCK! I LOST ALL MY MEN.

IF I HADN'T UNDERESTIMATED HIS POWERS, I COULD HAVE KILLED THE WHISPERER.

NOW IT'S TOO LATE TO ASK FOR MORE COMMANDOS. I NEED EMERGENCY TACTICS.

OOH! I CAN'T STAND IT! I HAVE TO CATCH A THIEF...

WHO STOLE MY HEART... TURN ON THE SIREN...!

EEEEE ¡¡E !

22

POOR ARCHIE. HE TOLD ME HE WANTED TO BE A WRITER.

THESE CHARACTERS... EITHER END UP LIKE HE DID OR WRITE NOVELS ABOUT STUFF THAT NEVER HAPPENED TO THEM.

EASY, PANAMA. RELAX.

UGH!

COMMISSIONER, THAT GUY WAS ARCHIE COOPER, A TWO-BIT PRIVATE EYE.

ANOTHER UNFORTUNATE.

HE GOT IN OVER HIS HEAD.

WHO'S THAT?

HEY! COMMISSIONER SINO HIMSELF..!!

GENTLEMEN, ALLOW ME TO INTRODUCE...

DON'T BOTHER. EVERYONE KNOWS ME. WHAT DO YOU KNOW ABOUT THE STIFF?

I DON'T ASK MY CUSTOMERS FOR RESUMES.

SO YOU ALSO DON'T KNOW ANYTHING ABOUT THE PARTY THIS AFTERNOON ON PIER NINE?

NOT MY SCENE, THANKS.

THATABOY.

23

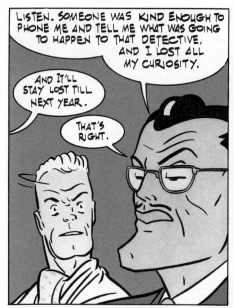

LISTEN. SOMEONE WAS KIND ENOUGH TO PHONE ME AND TELL ME WHAT WAS GOING TO HAPPEN TO THAT DETECTIVE, AND I LOST ALL MY CURIOSITY.

AND IT'LL STAY LOST TILL NEXT YEAR.

THAT'S RIGHT.

LET'S SEE IF I'VE GOT THIS STRAIGHT. A BIG SHOT SOLAR COMMISSIONER, MIXED UP IN DRUG DEALS, PUTS IN OVERTIME TO COME HERE AND TELL US A BUNCH OF LIES...

GROWL!

NOT YET! LET HIM YACK.

FORGET ALL ABOUT IT, MISTRAL. A CORPSE ATTRACTS ATTENTION. TWO WOULD BE LOUSY PUBLICITY FOR BUSINESS, AND THE THIRD COULD BE YOU.

WATCH YOUR BRAVE FRIEND.

YOU'RE NOT GOING TO GO ALONG WITH HIM, ARE YOU? I DIDN'T SEARCH FOR MY OLD PAL TO SEE HIM TAKE A THREAT SITTING DOWN.

GET OUT, PANAMA! ALL YOU'VE DONE IS BUG ME EVER SINCE YOU ARRIVED.

YOU WERE SITTING ON TOP OF THE WORLD, ROCCO. YOU COULD HAVE HAD THE SUN AND THEN ALL OF A SUDDEN...YOU DECIDED TO GET OLD.

BUT I'M NOT RUNNING. THE ERA OF SPACE RIDERS ISN'T OVER YET.

I'LL LEAVE TOMORROW.

WE'RE COMING TO THE "MONGO," SIR. THIS IS WHERE THE MURDER TOOK PLACE LAST NIGHT.

SO LONG, SAMSON. SAY GOOD BYE TO RUBY.

BYE, MR. PANAMA.

ROCCO, WE'VE GOT A LOT OF YEARS LEFT, BUT TIME IS RUNNING OUT.

EXCUSE MY CLUMSY INTERRUPTION.

...BUT MY IGNORANT PERSON WOULD LIKE TO KNOW WHICH OF YOU IS THE HONORABLE ARMANDO MISTRAL.

HE'S THE ONE WITH THE VENERABLE SOUR PUSS.

ALLOW ME TO INTRODUCE MYSELF. CHOP JONES, YOUR HUMBLE SERVANT.

JONES!

!

25

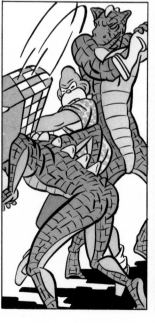

KIP?

THAT DETECTIVE WASN'T LYING. HE DIDN'T KNOW A THING. HE WAS JUST BAIT SO I COULD GET WITHIN RANGE OF THE WHISPERER.

A WASTE OF YOUR CHARMS!

THE WHISPERER? THAT VOICE ON THE PHONE!!

I'M FROM RHEA, WHICH YOU KNOW IS THE BIGGEST KROP-PRODUCING AREA IN THE SOLAR SYSTEM. SINCE THE WAR WITH VENUS BEGAN, THE KROP MARKET HAS BEEN LIKE A SACK WITH A GOLDEN SCORPION INSIDE. ONLY THE GREEDIEST ARE WILLING TO REACH INTO IT.

YOU TERRANS KNOW ALL ABOUT THESE THINGS. KROP ISN'T LEGAL HERE, BUT ONCE YOU'VE REFINED IT AND TURNED IT INTO ALUMAX, YOU SELL IT AT A HUNDRED TIMES THE PRICE AND LEGALIZE IT. WITH RHEA IN A STATE OF WAR, IT'S ALMOST IMPOSSIBLE TO GET TO THE KROP FIELDS OR THE REFINERIES. STOCKS ARE PILING UP AND THE PRICES ARE SKY HIGH.

IT'S AN EMPIRE WITHOUT AN EMPEROR. WHOEVER GETS CONTROL OF THE DISTRIBUTION WILL SCORE A BULL'S-EYE. THAT'S THE WHISPERER'S DREAM.

AND YOURS TOO.

28

NO, MY BROTHER GOT MIXED UP WITH HIM, AND NOW HE'S DEAD. IT'S MY DUTY TO AVENGE THE FAMILY HONOR.

AH! SO ARCHIE DIED FOR YOUR HONOR. HE'D HAVE ENJOYED KNOWING THAT.

LET'S NOT FORGET THEY KILLED HIM HERE.

BUT LISTEN. ALL I NEED IS A LITTLE AFFECTION AND SOME HELP. YOU SAW WHAT HAPPENED THIS MORNING. THE WHISPERER KNOWS WHERE I AM.

IN THIS SOAP OPERA YOU JUST TOLD US, MY DEAR YOUNG LADY,

YOU MEAN OURS!!

THERE'S ALSO A SOLAR COMMISSIONER WHO'S PLENTY MAD, AND NOT AT ME.

ARMANDO, WHAT HAPPENED LAST NIGHT?

TOO MUCH, RUBY.

HI! THERE!

?!

LET'S GO, HONEY. I NEED A DRESS.

AND AS FOR YOU, LOOK THROUGH THE KEYHOLE IF YOU WANT, BUT LEAVE ME ALONE!

HEE HEE.

COFFEE, SAMSON, COFFEE.

29

31

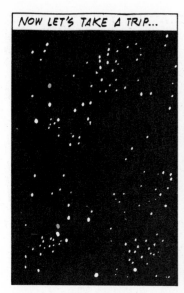

NOW LET'S TAKE A TRIP...

DESTINATION RHEA.

WE'RE HEADING FOR MEGAVENUS, THE SOUTHERN CAPITAL

WHILE ON VENUS – THE DISTANT COLONIAL POWER – PEACE TALKS CONTINUE, MEGAVENUS IS FULL OF REFUGEES, SOLDIERS, SPIES, AND MERCENARIES FROM THE ENTIRE SOLAR SYSTEM.

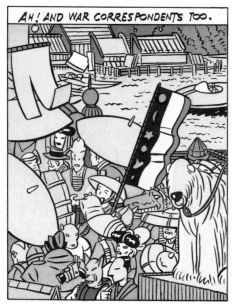

AH! AND WAR CORRESPONDENTS TOO.

MEANWHILE, ON EARTH.

TELL ME ABOUT HIM, PANAMA. I KNOW HE WAS A FAMOUS PILOT. WHY DID HE QUIT?

AH, THERE WERE THREE OF US. THEY CALLED US THE "SPACE KIDS". WE WERE YOUNG AND WILD. THAT'S WHY DOCTOR COVALSKY USED US TO START UP HIS "SPACE EXPRESS" SERVICE...

ROCCO WAS THE WILDEST. HE TAUGHT US TO LIVE SO FAST WE LEFT COMMON SENSE BEHIND. ALL KINDS OF THINGS HAPPENED. THAT RAT MUNG, BEAUTIFUL TATIANA, THE COLD WAR ... AND ONE DAY, ROCCO BUMPED INTO THE STARS.

BUMPED?

HE WANTED TO GO THERE, RUBY.

WHICH IS WHY HE'S UPSTAIRS, WRITING.

BUT IT'S IMPOSSIBLE. NO ROCKET CAN REACH THE STARS.

33

35

PANAMA, OLD BUDDY. I'M APPOINTING YOU MY AIDE-DE-CAMP. DRINK UP AND WE'LL GO INVADE THE GIRLS' DRESSING ROOM.

AH, JOE GUTI, YOU OLD LUSH. YEAH, YOU KNOW WHAT LIFE'S ALL ABOUT.

YOU WORK TOO HARD, GIRL.

YOU SEE, I'M THE ONE WHO REALLY MANAGES THE "MONGO."

AND YOU, WANTED TO MANAGE THE OWNER TOO, RIGHT?

LISTEN, DON'T GET MAD, BUT IF YOU WANT HIM TO NOTICE YOU, YOU'LL HAVE TO DO SOMETHING MORE EXCITING THAN PORING OVER BILLS.

HOW DARE YOU?

SHOW HIM THERE'S A WOMAN HIDING BEHIND THOSE GLASSES. I'VE GOT A JOB FOR YOU TONIGHT THAT'LL MAKE HIM PAY ATTENTION.

BUT IF HIS ADMIRATION ISN'T ENOUGH, MAYBE SOME MONEY...

34

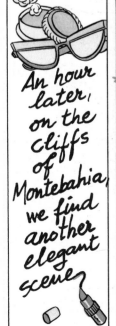

37

LET'S SEE...

SCARLET TOLD ME THERE SHOULD BE A HIDDEN DOOR OVER THERE.

AND INDEED, ONCE RUBY IS ALONE...

36

Fans ?!

I'LL SWALLOW MY CURIOSITY, LEAVE THE PACKAGE AND GET OUT.

LATER, JUST BEFORE DAWN...

SILK, COCKTAILS, AND MY FEET... HIC! DOOBIE DOOBIE DA... TRAPPED!

KIIP! ? ?

LISTEN, DUMBBELL: I COULDN'T FINISH OFF THE WHISPERER AT "HEROES AND PIRATES." I FOUND ANOTHER TRAIL THAT LED TO AN ALUMAX JOINT CALLED THE "DOMINO," BUT I COULD NEVER SHOW MY FACE THERE. I NEEDED SOME SWEET, INNOCENT SOUL, AND THAT GIRL CAME ALONG AT THE RIGHT TIME.

... I DID IT FOR MY BROTHER.

THE HELL WITH YOUR FAMILY!! ALL I CARE ABOUT IS GETTING RUBY OUT OF THERE.

I THINK IT'S TIME FOR ACTION!

GET YOUR SHIP READY, PANAMA.

IT'LL ONLY TAKE A SECOND.

LET'S GO!

YOU'RE STAYING! I DON'T WANT AMATEURS AROUND.

OH!

TRAC!

LET GO OF ME, YOU BASTARD! COCKROACH! PUNK!

HANG ON TO THIS KEY, AND DON'T TAKE YOUR EYES OFF HER.

PIMP! SEWER RAT!

39

41

42

45

JOE GUTI TOLD ME WHERE IT WAS HIDDEN WHILE HE WAS STRUGGLING WITH MY ZIPPER, AND I WAS HOLDING THE KEY TO MY HANDCUFFS FOR HIM.

SHUP UP! SAVE YOUR JOKES FOR JAIL!

I WARNED YOU, MISTRAL.

YOUR ANTICS DON'T SCARE ME, COMMISSIONER. THEY JUST PIQUE MY CURIOSITY, AND WHEN THAT HAPPENS, I HURRY OVER TO CHAT WITH SOME VERY NOSY JOURNALISTS I'M FRIENDS WITH.

VERY GOOD!

YOU REALIZE HOW MUCH DANGER RUBY WAS IN?

YES, THE POOR DEAR. SHE LOOKS TERRIBLY UPSET.

SHE GOT WHAT SHE WANTED. BY THE WAY, WHAT DID YOU DO WITH THAT BOMB?

THE BOMB!

BAUM

45